The Boys' Own BATTLE OF BRITAIN

by

with & from

PETER CROSS

PAVILION

The boys would like to thank :

Mr Len Deighton for his wizard book 'Battle of Britain', which was an inspiration.

Mr Peter Dallas-Smith, who had some ripping ideas, and was always willing to help with homework. (And not forgetting Dame Betty's super lunchtime concerts.)

All the Staff of the 'Ops Room', Fighter Command (Boys' Own Wing) and in particular : Group Captain Ken Leigh-Webb, Squadron Leader Red 'Socks Away' Russell, and on secondment from the LUFTWAAF, Fräulein Rippintrop ~ one time German Foreign Minister and architect of the Nazi-Soviet Cyclists' Pact, and now believed to be living in Peckham.

Miss Rachel, the School Welfare Officer, for keeping Timothy quiet during raids.

Crown Litho, Godalming, for being allowed to 'go solo' on the Photocopier.

And good luck to Mr Pickles, the Artmaster, and the Ryder Street Academy for young ladies. Hope the show goes well in June.

First published in 1989 by
PAVILION BOOKS LIMITED
196 Shaftesbury Avenue, London WC2H 8JL.

A CIP catalogue record for this book is
available from the British Library

ISBN 1 85145 378 4

10 9 8 7 6 5 4 3 2 1

Printed in Hong Kong
by South China Printing Company

金燕

宝云

When St Hitla's was founded in 1933, its aim was to become the biggest school in the world.

SPORTS DAY AT St HITLA'S, 1936

The Principal, Dr Adolphus, was keen on sport, and the trophy-room soon began to fill up.

By the end of the decade, the School had built up a formidable reputation both on and off the field.

They were dubbed 'THE BROWN SHORTS' after the distinctive colour of their knickerbockers

When the 1940 season started, there were comfortable victories over

They were on a winning streak

through the fiords & birch forests of St Olafs

Danes Hill,

St Olaf's,

Holland Park

and

King Leopold's.

Their PANZIES put on a show

They had a tremendously effective front row

'We're going to take down the washing on the Siegfried Line'

'Nothing can-can stop them now.'

It was looking like a whitewash

Notre Dame were expected to put up a fight, but they were easily dispatched, and now, only the boys of Biggin Hill stood between St Hitla's and an unprecedented clean sweep.

They were 'Champs de Lycées' in no time

By contrast, Biggin Hill's season had gone rather badly, and a new Headmaster had been appointed.

Mr Winston wasted no time in discussing tactics with his Housemasters for the coming match.

Mr Leigh-Mullery wanted to play all the boys on the wing in one large formation ~ the so-called 'Big Wings' theory.

As a goodwill gesture, Mr Winston wanted the game played at Notre Dame.

But Mr Dowdy, the Senior Housemaster, had his own plan and he was sticking to it. They were his boys, and he was not going to see years of careful preparation thrown away in an afternoon. Besides, he was retiring at the end of term, and he was determined to go out on a win.

AIR/SEA RESCUE

MR HYDE-PARK

e Pew

· ATTEMPTING A DRY RUN IN THE SCHOOL CHAPEL ·
(After Matins)

used to

LOOPING THE LOOP

ORIGINAL SQUAD 52

NOW DOWN TO 26

On the morning before the match, Mr Hyde-Park, the Games Master, put the boys through their paces.

★ Practicing with planes would have been better, but Mr Dowdy didn't want to lose any more machines in needless prangs.

5

The boys were told to tighten up their formations, and they returned to the classroom for extra lessons.

SOME FORMATIONS THROUGH THE AGES

THE TESTUDO
(GALLIC WARS ~ 58 to 51 BC)

THE SQUARE
(BLENHEIM ~ 1704)

THE VIC
(BATTLE OF BRITAIN ~1940)

In spite of St Hitla's success with the new 4-2-4 system, Biggin still stuck to the old 'Vic' formation.

VICS
SOOTHING, DEPENDABLE...
RUB IN THOROUGHLY LAST THING AT NIGHT
BEST BEFORE: SEPT 1939

When it came to the lesson on Aerodynamics, the boys had some ideas of their own.

MAKE YOUR OWN WIND DIRECTION INDICATORS
WIND SOCK
WIND COMBINATIONS
WIND BAG (MATRON)
WIND IN THE WILLOWS
Strength of Fighter Command at the time of Munich

HOW TO MAKE A FOLDED PAPER SPITFIRE
with Chris and Val

"And here's one I made earlier."

BLUE PETER OLD SOCKS APPEAL
John, Jason, Peter and Petra with a Mk II Spitfire made out of 300,000 pairs of old socks!

The class was interrupted by the Headmaster who announced that there was to be a School outing in the afternoon.

Instead of 'Sinking into the abyss of a new Dark Age, made more sinister and perhaps more protracted by the lights of perverted science' (History followed by Physics and Chemistry), they could all 'move forward into broad sunlit uplands' in a special Double Art class, taken by Mr Winston himself.

6

YIPEE!

The outing, to the local airfield, proved a tremendous success, and afterwards a selection of work was put on display in the School Hall.

BACON, F.

HILLIARD, N.

STUBBS, G.

SPENCER, S.

NASH, P.

PALMER, S.

LICHTENSTEIN, R.

HOCKNEY, D.

MOORE, H

NICHOLSON, B.

HEATH ROBINSON, W.

SUTHERLAND, G.

Back at school, preparations for the
Big Match continued well into the evening.

After a hot bath and a mug of cocoa, the boys settled down for an early night.

KANAL KAMPF
(CHANNEL BATTLE)
SHIPPING IN THE CHANNEL COMES UNDER ATTACK FROM ENEMY DIVE BOMBERS— THE FIRST STAGE OF THE BATTLE OF BRITAIN.

(A) STUKA ABOUT TO BOMB MERCHANTMAN.
(B) CAPTAIN OF MERCHANTMAN CALLS FOR ASSISTANCE.
(C) BLENHEIM OF COASTAL COMMAND PREPARES TO SCRAMBLE.

'RADOX'
The bath salts that give you early warning of approaching aches and planes.

'Put out that light!'

BOFORS ANTI-AIRCRAFT GUN

Not many went to sleep though.

There were secret dens under the sheets...

'Dan'

PARABELLUM -A.E. -O

'ENIGMA' DE-CODING MACHINE

ELGAR I C.A.E. / II H.D.S-P. / III R.B.T. / IV W.M.B. / V R.P.A. / VI YSOBEL / VII TROYTE / VIII W.N. / IX NIMROD

ENIGMA VARIATIONS

THE MALVERNS

SUSSEX

SPECIALLY PREPARED RED CROSS FOOD BASKET

MI5 All-purpose escaper's penknife

Escaped pet hamster

BROCK'S SHERBET FOUNTAIN

MIDGET GOLF

MECCANO

French Country Pâté with Brandy

VINTAGE APPLE & MINT JELLY

SUGARED ALMONDS

A dead beetle

Conker

'HERMANN THE GERMAN' ® PYJAMA CASE
Mischievous head of the Luftwaffe in soft velour with squeak & hanging ribbon PLUS pop-out Luftflotte 2

A Selection of favourite marbles

Sunbeam Clockwork Racer

SUNBEAM

· Equipping Your Secret Den / Underground Air Raid Shelter / Confidential Hidy-Hole / Spitfire Cockpit etc ·

and impromptu aircraft recognition displays...

SPITFIRE

MESSERSCHMITT

FOKKER

HEINKEL (with its port engine on fire & pilot just about to bale out)

They had to be careful ▷

FLOOR

DORM

In the dispersal lounge, the Duty Masters prepared for a surprise dormitory patrol by wearing special night acclimatization goggles.

It was midnight before everyone had quietened down.

z z z z Z Z Z z z   z z Z Z z z z

10

Through the open window of the staff common-room, Mr Hyde-Park heard the unmistakable hum of Merlins in the distance.

It was the dawn patrol returning, and he rushed outside to count them in.

DE-BRIEFING — Note the new 'V' fronts

'Ginger' fashioned elaborate dog-fights with swooping hands.

The de-briefing which followed soon revealed that the opposition had already set off and were making good time.

At assembly, the Headmaster roused the School with a terrific speech.

The boys cheered and quickly scrambled.

11

⬧ St Hitla's arrive ⬧

When they saw the turn-off for Biggin Hill, St Hitla's stamped their feet and chanted the School song.

The huge Junkers pulled up outside the School gates and the students piled off.

They were an arrogant lot.

'Biggin Hill will be done
At the end of Round One!'

LOOK,
NO HANS!

Rottweiler ®
XXX
EXTRA STRONG
EXPORT
Lager
shandy

Nodding
sausage
dog

Fluffy dice

SIEGFRIED
UND
BRÜNHILDA

ICH ♥ STURM UND PRANG

Their pack was full of aces
~ including the N°1 seed.

Close-up of a
ONE O'NINE
cockpit

A ♠

A ♥ MOULDERS

A ♥ GALLARD

A ♦ VICK

JOKER

Zigger Zagger Zigger Zagger

Oi Oi Oi!

Exciting marching songs
were followed by an unusual
pre-match warm-up routine.

♦ SYNCHRONISED KNEE-SLAPPING ♦

St Hitla's won the toss★ and elected to open the attack.

◆ BIGGIN HILL ◆	St Hitla's	◆ St HITLA'S ◆
Blue Blazers	ADOLPHS 1940 → ADOLPHS 1940	Horrid Brown Stripey Tops
Cream Flannels	Double-headed	" " " Bottoms
Grey Stockings	Pfennig	Yellow Stockings, Brown Suspenders
		Dappled Grey Underparts
		Mottled Green Fuselage

First away were the Stukas. They swept across the playing-fields heading for the Biggin Hill *High Frequency Direction Finding Station*.

St HITLA'S St HITLA'S RA RA RA !

'SMILING' ALBERT KETTLERI
GRÖSS TOSSER
14 Stone

'SCOWLING' HUGO SPERRL
GRÖSS TOSSER
16 Stone

GIANT HESSTACKS
OBERGRÖSSTOSSER
17 Stone

BIG
BADDY

FATTY GORING
OBERGRÖSSMARSCHALLTOSSE
20 Stone

The Stukas unleashed their deadly load of stink bombs on the Biggin boys, who were taken by surprise.

HIGH FREQUENCY DIRECTION FINDING
(KEEPING CAVE)

'PIPSQUEAK'

HOW IT WORKED

Enemy activity set up a chorus of chirruping squeaks amongst the cavies. The squeaks were transmitted to the main building where Mr Dowdy and the Science Master Mr Watson-Watt, monitored the signals in the cupboard under the stairs.

WE CAN TAKE IT !

The bombs were real stinkers, but the youngsters knew their drill, and they quickly set up alternative lines of communication. ▶

TELEPHONE TELEPHONE

DUXFORD
HAWKINGE
FORTHCHURCH
KENLEY
MANSTON
NORTHOLT
TH WEALD
PEMBREY
ROCHFORD
SIDCUP
S† EVAL
TANGMERE
WARMWELL

A-D
E
L
K
P

STINK BOMBS — Know Your Drill

1 Take out your gasmask

2 Put it on.

✓ CORRECT   ✗ INCORRECT

· MICKEY MASKS ·

15

'Bandits on their way!'

In the second attack, the enemy made for the groundsman's hut.

'Roger Rabbit Leader, out.'

Hurricanes were scrambled, but in the excitement an Atco trainer was shot down by mistake.

Observers rifled through their Pedal Plane Recognition Books

St Hitla's
BMW 110 'zerstörer' (The Destroyer)

Mr Pyle
The Head Groundsman

The cricket pavilion was the next target, only this time a large number of Stukas came under fire from the orchard, where Mr Pyle's *pommes pommes* were in a good position*.

Mr Pyle's Pommes Pommes & Heavy Bofors Brigade

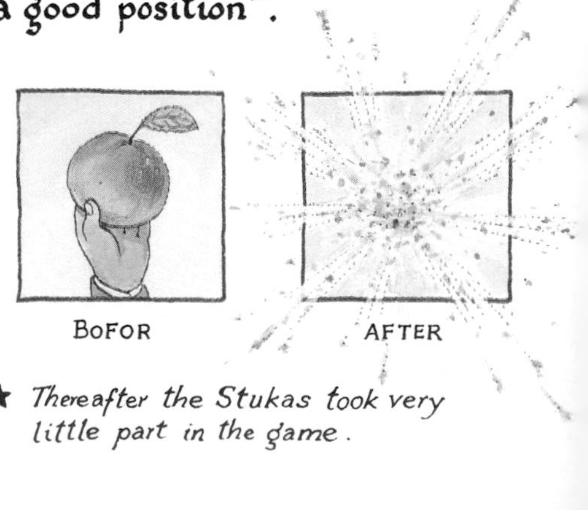

BOFOR

AFTER

★ Thereafter the Stukas took very little part in the game.

16

THE CHMITT BROTHERS ~ First to pedal the channel in their much vaunted ONE O'NINE

Mr MITCHELL~ Designer of the famous SPITFIRE (probably the most graceful pedal plane ever built)

Of all St Hitla's planes, the One O'Nine was the fastest and most formidable. But it had its match in the Spitfire, which was just as fast and could turn on a sixpence →

MESSERS CHMITT 109

Spitfire

A shortage of Spitfires early in the game weakened the Biggin defence, so Lord Beavers who was on the Board of Governors, organised a wizard 'Saucepans into Spitfires' campaign.

Daily Express LORD BEAVERS TO THE RESCUE

A similar 'Hockey Sticks into Hurricanes' campaign never got off the ground

With all the saucepans used up, lunch was a packet of crisps and a bottle of cherry cider ▷

For most of the morning, the shark-nosed One O'Nines had milled menacingly round the front gates trying to draw Biggin into a scrap. Outnumbered nearly four to one, Mr Dowdy knew better than to try and take them on at their own game. He had to husband his resources carefully and prepare for the inevitable onslaught to come.

He didn't have to wait long. After lunch, the monitor picked up something unusually big.
It could only mean one thing...

17

Mr Dowdy had a spiffing collection of gold cuff links

... *Bovvers !*

Through the gates they came and down the drive, heading for the bicycle sheds.

There was a terrific scramble.

Many boys came off their bikes and there were some nasty injuries.

Mr Dowdy's Rotation System

An attempt to keep the boys fresh and on their toes

Finding replacements for injured players was now Mr Dowdy's main concern.

Overseas students on exchange visits had been told that they could take part in the game provided they finished their English Grammars first. Well there was no time for grammar now, they would have to play straight away.

An Aborigine Spitfire
~Note the wing-mounted poison blow-pipes

FRAN JANAČEK
(Top scorer)

They did better than anyone had expected and finished up among the top scorers for the Home side.

CAPS OF OVERSEAS STUDENTS

St Zloty

King Wenceslas

Notre Dame

Eaglets

King Leopold's

THE EMPIRE HELPS OUT

Kiwigo Kiwigo Kiwigo

Maple Leaf Mounties

Springboks

St Matilda's

HOME CAPS

1st XI

COLOURS 2nd XI

Under XI

Under Age

Under Cover

Under Pants

Under dog

Under Arrest

SOME CONFISCATED ENEMY CAPS

Twirly-whirly

Toothaches?

caramel

Bier stalker

zebra

Hot-Cross Bun

Tutti Frutti

(ceremonial)

zig-zag

19

Then, bad light stopped play and everyone came off for tea.

HIGH TEA

THE NATIONAL TRUST
HURRICANE APPEAL
Help grow another one

Pancakes
Victory Rolls
Jelly Flops
Hot Dog-
Fights
HONEY WITH
EVERYTHING

In the Staff Common Room, they were down to the last of the angel cakes and there was a bit of a scramble on.

MR STANFORD'S Travelling TUCK SHOP

AERO MILK CHOCOLATE

LACEY'S GINGERS MADE IN YORKSHIRE

LIQUORICE ALL SORTIES

SPANGLES PARACHUTE DROPS

BANDIT

BIRD'S PISTOL WHIP

HACK HACK COUGH SWEETS
FOR AA GUNNERS

◆ ANGELS ONE FIVE ◆

◀ Douglas Dada, House Prefect and Captain of Collage, had a wonderful collection of 'Big Wings' which he went round showing everybody...

BATTLE OF BRITAIN BIG WINGS

21

BRIGHTON BELLE

CAMBERWELL BEAUTY

ENEMY PARACHUTIST

BIGGIN HILL BLUE

PEACOCK

DOVER PATROL

SPOTTED DICK

BADDY LONG LEGS

HERCULES BRABAZON BRABAZON

TIGER MOTH BALL

DEATH'S HEAD PICKLEHAUBE

BRITAIN

WINGS

Meanwhile, 'Fatty' Goring, St Hitla's Head Boy and the School Bully, paced the floor of the Junkers Trimotor.

The match should have been won by now. Time was running out and Dr Adolfus wanted a result quickly.

St Hitla's Heavy Tea

JAGDPANTHER Self Propelled Chocolate Eclair

BATTENBURG Pocket Battle-cake

BERLIN WEATHER CENTRE

HILVERSUM LUXEMBURG BERLIN SIDCUP

'There vill be no Hurricanes'

The forecast after tea was good, so rather than waiting to finish off the bicycle sheds, 'Fatty' decided to deliver a devastating 'coup de grass' on the croquet lawn.

MALLETS AFORETHOUGHT

In a grandstand finish, hordes of black-cross Bovvers cut a swath across the neatly trimmed lawn.

CHAMPING AT THE BIT

Mr Leigh-Mullery waited impatiently in the wings for his chance to come on.

But the change in tactics by St Hitla's was a crucial mistake. The bicycle sheds were given a vital respite and Mr Dowdy's boys (*their Hurricanes repaired*) were able to hold the line.

From the air, a pattern began to emerge

The crowd was kept in touch with the scores as they came in, which was handy.

TICK-TACK WINNIE

TANGMERE	1	St EVAL
MANSTON	X	
HAWKINGE	X	KENLEY
NORTH WEALD	2	ROCHFORD
WEST MALLING	1	FULHAM
NORTHOLT	2	DUXFORD
HORNCHURCH	1	MIDDLE WALLOP
	X	MARTLESHAM
	2	PEMBREY
	1	WARMWELL

And then, with only five minutes to go, on came Mr Leigh-Mullery and his

BIG WINGS

The opposition suddenly didn't want to play anymore.

They trooped off the pitch at the final whistle.

They didn't even wait to exchange shorts.

26

The Umpires collected the scores and rushed them over to the gym where they were added up.

After several recounts, the result was announced:

'I, the Returning Officer for the World, Northern Hemisphere, hereby declare the Winners to be...

BIGGIN HILL!'

St Hitla's had lost their unbeaten record and there were jubilant scenes!

Not everyone on the Home Side was happy though. In spite of the success of Mr Dowdy's skilfully co-ordinated defence, some said the 'Big Wings' should have been brought on earlier.

Anyway, the Head was over the moon and he made a tremendous speech to the School.

'Nunquam in campus de pugno humano erat tantum debit ad multum a tam pauci.'

The translation was something like ▶

'The having been defeated St Hitla's... The lads did magic and extra half hols all round!'

The celebrations started immediately and went on well into the night.

Mind you, that was
not quite the end of it.
(*It wasn't the beginning either, but
only the end of the beginning.*)
Before they left, 'Fatty' Goring
and a few of his cronies let off
some fireworks outside
the School gates.

It was rather an effective display.

◆

◀ The rockets were way ahead of their time.

Doodlebug

28

One rocket dropped through the door of the science lab where Whittle and a number of his chums were working late. But the youngsters were so absorbed in their experiment that they hardly noticed.

And when another rocket hit the outside of the Headmaster's study, badly blackening the brickwork and cracking the mortar in places, Mr Winston himself dashed out and helped in the re-pointing.

'Give me the tools and I'll finish the job.'

No one was hurt, and the celebrations were not effected.

DOWDY FOREVER

PER ARDUA AD ASTRA

When the excitement had died down and the full extent of Biggin's achievement was realised, it was decided to decorate the School Chapel with a series of romantic frescos.

The delicate watercolours were of course, all the *Boys' Own* work, and commemorated a victory that they were proud to call

'*Their Finest Hour.*'

This happy breed of boys, this little School; This outfit of Spits, this Few; This bandit at 4 o'clock, this wizard prang; This chocolate cupcake, this England

BRILLIANT, UNFADING LIGHT

POWDER BLUE SKY

GOLDEN, RADIANT SUMMER

1940

SWIRLING VAPOUR TRAILS

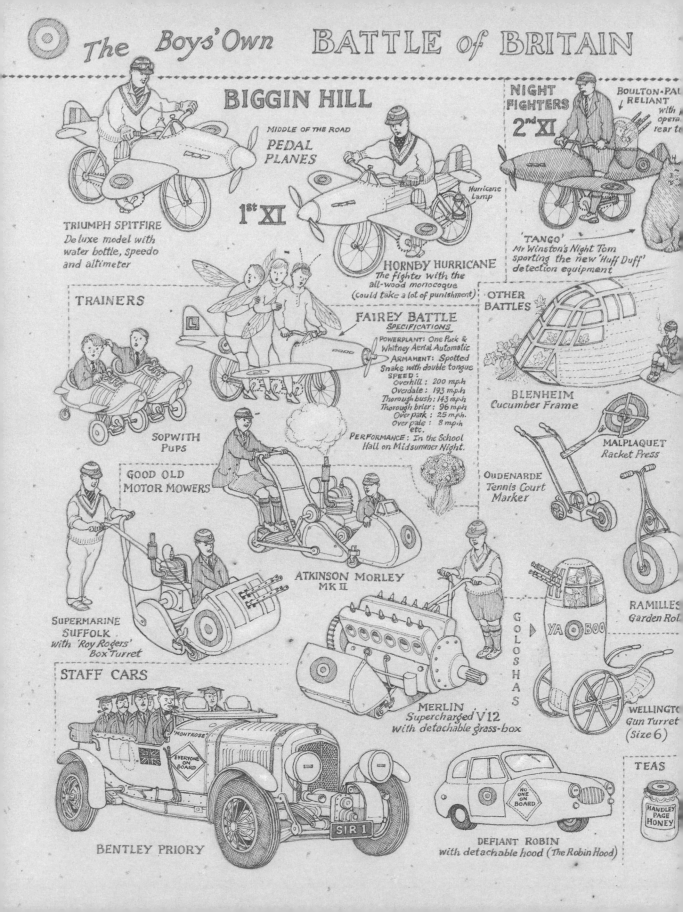

The Boys' Own BATTLE of BRITAIN

BIGGIN HILL

MIDDLE OF THE ROAD
PEDAL PLANES

1st XI

TRIUMPH SPITFIRE
De luxe model with water bottle, speedo and altimeter

Hurricane Lamp

HORNBY HURRICANE
The fighter with the all-wood monocoque (could take a lot of punishment)

NIGHT FIGHTERS 2nd XI

BOULTON-PAUL RELIANT
with opera... rear t...

'TANGO'
Mr Winston's Night Tom sporting the new 'Huff Duff' detection equipment

TRAINERS

SOPWITH Pups

FAIREY BATTLE
SPECIFICATIONS
POWERPLANT: One Puck & Whitney Aerial Automatic
ARMAMENT: Spotted Snake with double tongue
SPEED:
Overhill : 200 m.p.h
Ovadale : 193 m.p.h
Thorough bush : 143 m.p.h
Thorough brier : 96 m.p.h
Over park : 25 m.p.h
Over pale : 8 m.p.h
etc.
PERFORMANCE : In the School Hall on Midsummer Night.

OTHER BATTLES

BLENHEIM
Cucumber Frame

MALPLAQUET
Racket Press

OUDENARDE
Tennis Court Marker

GOOD OLD MOTOR MOWERS

ATKINSON MORLEY MK II

SUPERMARINE SUFFOLK
with 'Roy Rogers' Box Turret

MERLIN
Supercharged V12 with detachable grass-box

GOLOSHAS

YA-BOO

RAMILLES
Garden Rol...

WELLINGTO...
Gun Turret (Size 6)

STAFF CARS

'MONTROSE'
EVERYONE ON BOARD
SIR 1

BENTLEY PRIORY

DEFIANT ROBIN
with detachable hood (The Robin Hood)

NO ONE ON BOARD

TEAS

HANDLEY PAGE HONEY